EASIEST
KEYBOARD
COLLECTION

Pop Classics

WISE PUBLICATIONS
London/New York/Paris/Sydney/Copenhagen/Madrid

Exclusive Distributors:

Music Sales Limited
8/9 Frith Street,
London W1V 5TZ, England.

Music Sales Pty Limited
120 Rothschild Avenue,
Rosebery, NSW 2018,
Australia..

Order No. AM944196
ISBN 0-7119-6601-X
This book © Copyright 1997 by Wise Publications

Cover design by Chloë Alexander
Compiled by Peter Evans
Music arranged by Derek Jones
Music processed by Paul Ewers Music Design

Printed in the United Kingdom by
Caligraving Limited, Thetford, Norfolk.

Cover photograph courtesy of:
Image Bank

Your Guarantee of Quality
As publishers, we strive to produce every book to the highest commercial
standards.
The music has been freshly engraved and the book has been carefully
designed to minimise awkward page turns and to make playing from it a
real pleasure.
Particular care has been given to specifying acid-free, neutral-sized paper
made from pulps which have not been elemental chlorine bleached. This
pulp is from farmed sustainable forests and was produced with special
regard for the environment.
Throughout, the printing and binding have been planned to ensure a
sturdy, attractive publication which should give years of enjoyment.
If your copy fails to meet our high standards, please inform us and we will
gladly replace it.

Music Sales' complete catalogue describes thousands of titles and is
available in full colour sections by subject, direct from Music Sales
Limited. Please state your areas of interest and send a cheque/postal
order for £1.50 for postage to: Music Sales Limited, Newmarket Road,
Bury St. Edmunds, Suffolk IP33 3YB.

Contents

A WHITER SHADE OF PALE

Words & Music by Keith Reid & Gary Brooker

Voice: **Electric organ**

Rhythm: **Ballad**

Tempo: ♩ = 84

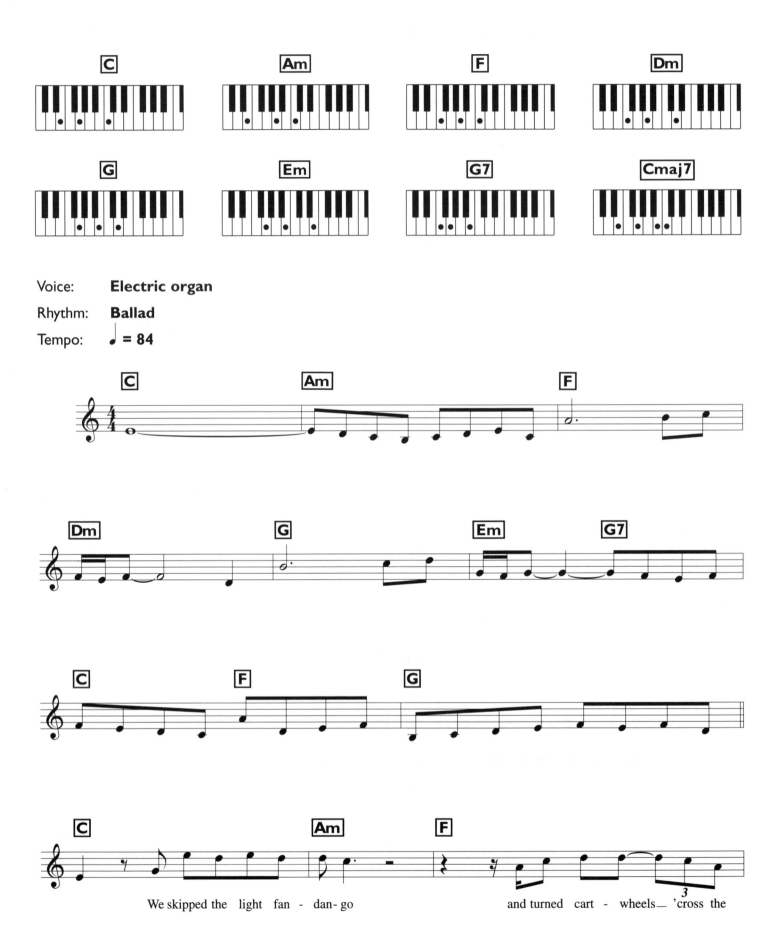

We skipped the light fan-dan-go   and turned cart-wheels— 'cross the

floor.— I was feel - ing kind of sea - sick,

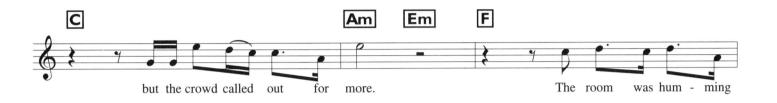

but the crowd called out for more. The room was hum - ming

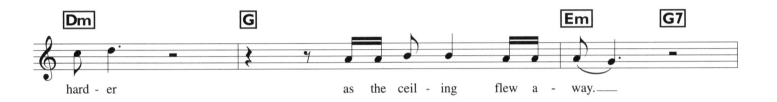

hard - er as the ceil - ing flew a - way.—

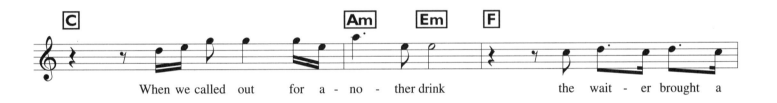

When we called out for a - no - ther drink the wait - er brought a

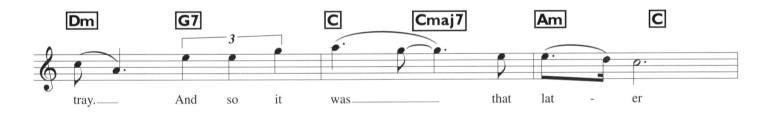

tray.— And so it was——— that lat - er

as the mill - er told his tale—— that her face, at first just

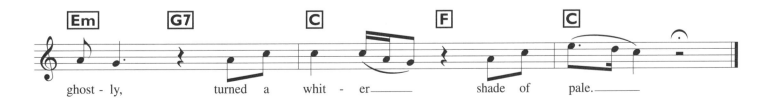

ghost - ly, turned a whit - er—— shade of pale.———

BRIDGE OVER TROUBLED WATER

Words & Music by Paul Simon

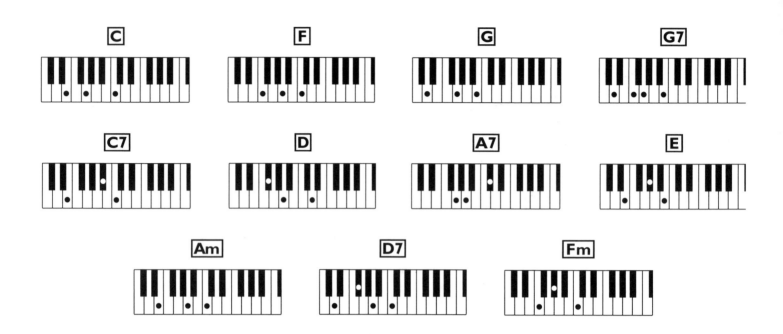

Voice: **Strings**

Rhythm: **Ballad**

Tempo: ♩ = 80

When you're wea - ry, feel - in'

small, when tears are in your

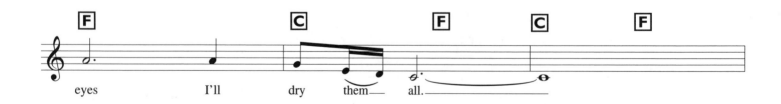

eyes I'll dry them all.

CECILIA

Words & Music by Paul Simon
© Copyright 1969, 1970 Paul Simon.
All Rights Reserved. International Copyright Secured.

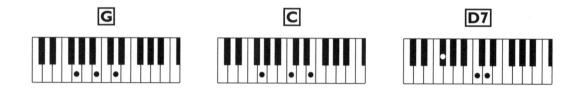

Voice: **Clarinet**

Rhythm: **8 Beat**

Tempo: ♩ = 108

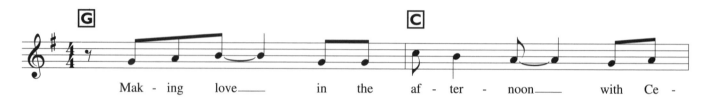

Mak - ing love____ in the af - ter - noon____ with Ce -

- ce - lia up____ in my bed - room.____ I got up____ to

wash my face____ when I come back to bed____ some-one's tak - en my place.____

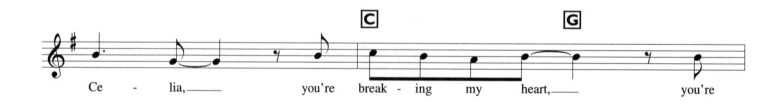

Ce - lia,____ you're break - ing my heart,____ you're

shak - ing my con - fi - dence dai - ly.____ Oh Ce -

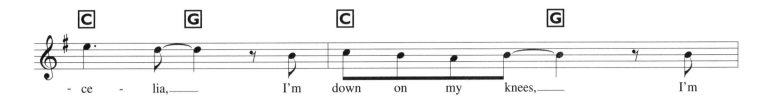

- ce - lia, _____ I'm down on my knees, _____ I'm

beg - ging you please___ to come home, _____ ho ho home. _____ Poh poh

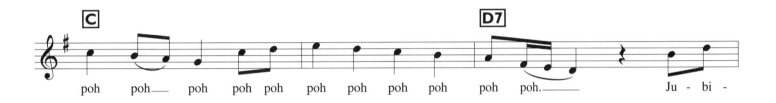

poh poh___ poh poh poh poh poh poh poh poh poh._____ Ju - bi -

- la - tion, _____ she loves me a gain, _____ I fall on the floor___ and I'm laugh-

- ing. _____ Ju - bi - la - tion, ___ she loves me a - gain, ___ I

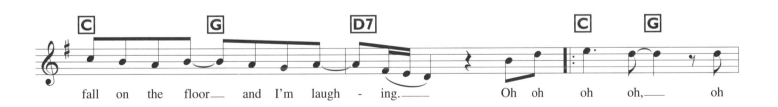

fall on the floor___ and I'm laugh - ing. _____ Oh oh oh oh, _____ oh

Repeat to fade

oh oh oh oh, _____ oh oh oh oh oh___ oh oh oh. Oh oh

CROCODILE ROCK

Words & Music by Elton John & Bernie Taupin

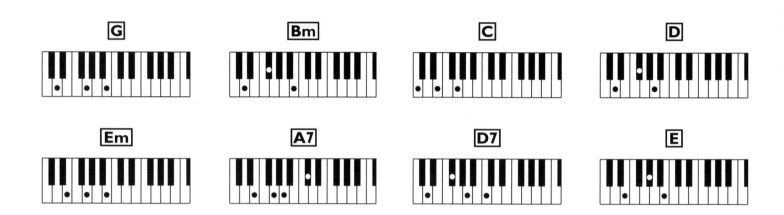

Voice: **Saxophone**

Rhythm: **Rock**

Tempo: ♩ = 132

I re-mem-ber when Rock was young,_____ me and Su-

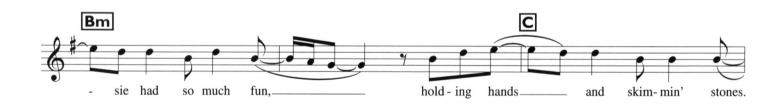

-sie had so much fun,_____ hold-ing hands_____ and skim-min' stones.

_____ Had an old gold Che-vy and a place of my own.__ But the big-

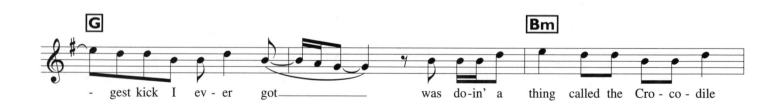

-gest kick I ev-er got_____ was do-in' a thing called the Cro-co-dile

Rock._____ While the oth - er kids were Rock-in' round the Clock,— we were hop-

- pin' and bop - pin' to the Cro - co - dile Rock. Went Cro-co-dile Rock-in' is

some - thing shock - in' when your feet just can't keep still.— I ne-ver knew me a

bet-ter time— and I guess— I ne - ver— will.— Oh___ lau-dy ma-ma those

Fri - day nights— when Su - sie wore her dres-ses tight___ and the Cro-co-dile— rock-in'

was____ out of sight._____

Repeat to fade

EVERY BREATH YOU TAKE

Words & Music by Sting

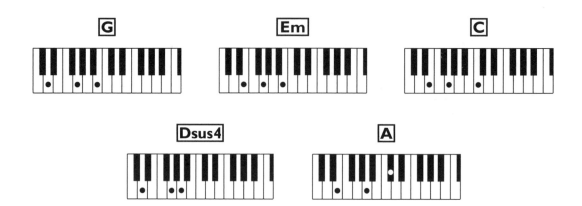

Voice: **Clarinet**

Rhythm: **Soft Rock**

Tempo: ♩ = 100

Ev - ery breath you___ take and ev - ery move you___

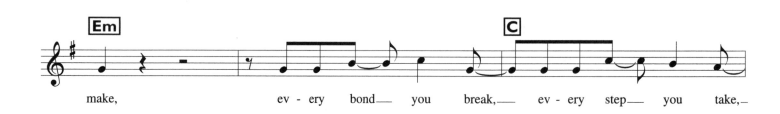

make, ev - ery bond___ you break,___ ev - ery step___ you take,___

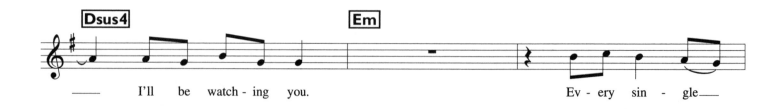

___ I'll be watch - ing you. Ev - ery sin - gle___

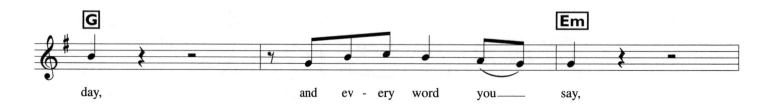

day, and ev - ery word you___ say,

ev-ery game— you play,— ev-ery night— you stay,— I'll be watch-ing you.

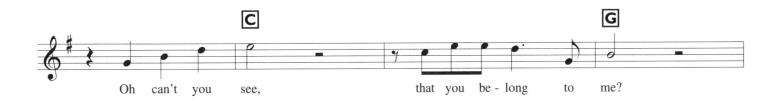

Oh can't you see, that you be - long to me?

My— poor heart— aches— with ev-ery step— you take.

Ev-ery move you— make and ev-ery vow you— break,

ev-ery smile— you fake,— ev-ery claim— you stake,— I'll be watch-ing you.

Ev-ery move— you make,— ev-ery step— you take,— I'll be watch-ing you.

Repeat to fade

HE AIN'T HEAVY...HE'S MY BROTHER

Words by Bob Russell
Music by Bobby Scott
© Copyright 1969 by Harrison Music Corporation, USA & Jenny Music.
Chelsea Music Publishing Company Limited, 70 Gloucester Place, London W1H 4AJ/Jenny Music.
All Rights Reserved. International Copyright Secured.

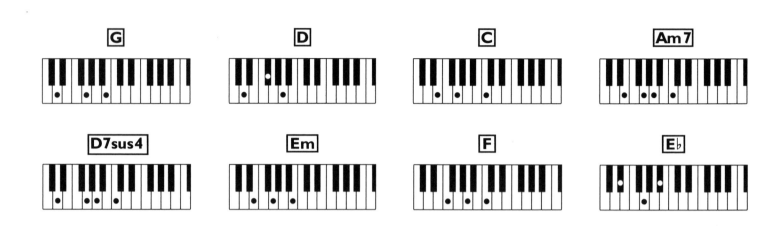

Voice: **Electric Organ**

Rhythm: **16 Beat**

Tempo: ♩ = 76

The road is long

with ma - ny a wind - ing turn,

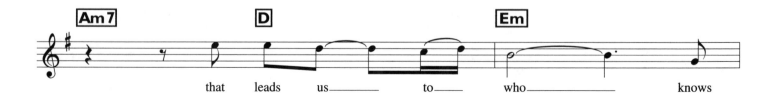

that leads us to who knows

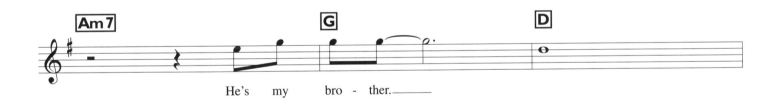

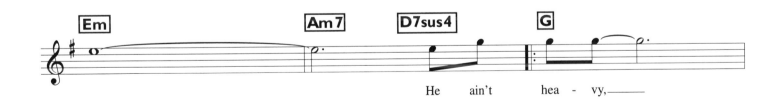

HEARTBREAKER

Words & Music by Barry Gibb, Robin Gibb & Maurice Gibb

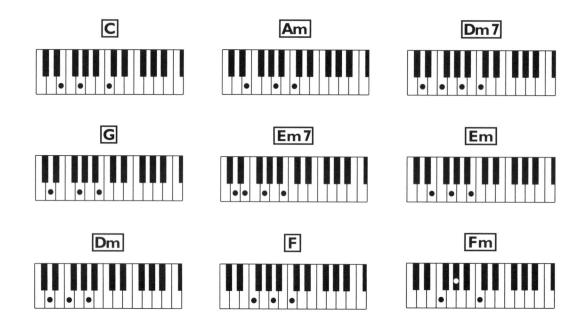

Voice: **Trumpet**

Rhythm: **Rock**

Tempo: ♩ = 104

I have to say it and it's hard for me.

You got me cry-in' like I thought I would ne-ver be, love is be-liev-in', but

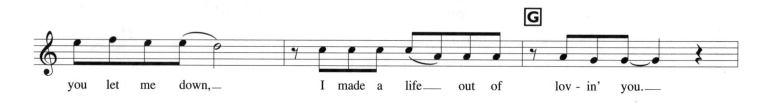

you let me down,— I made a life— out of lov-in' you.—

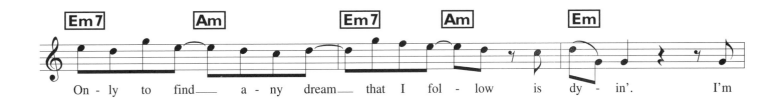

On - ly to find—— a - ny dream—— that I fol - low is dy - in'. I'm

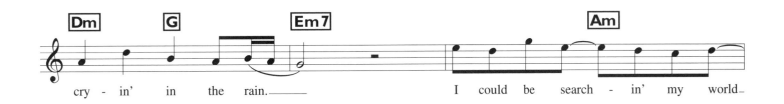

cry - in' in the rain.—— I could be search - in' my world——

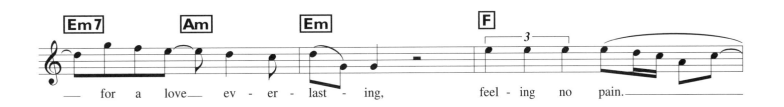

—— for a love—— ev - er - last - ing, feel - ing no pain.——

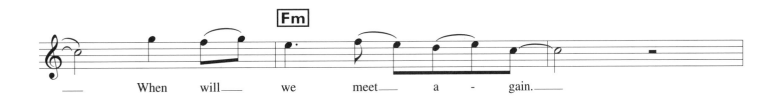

—— When will—— we meet—— a - gain.——

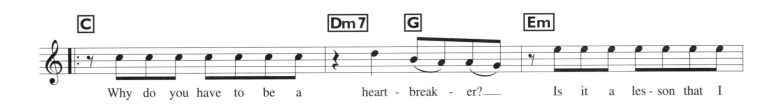

Why do you have to be a heart - break - er?—— Is it a les - son that I

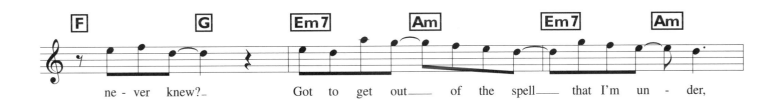

ne - ver knew?— Got to get out—— of the spell—— that I'm un - der,

Repeat to fade

my love for you.——

HEY JUDE

Words & Music by John Lennon & Paul McCartney

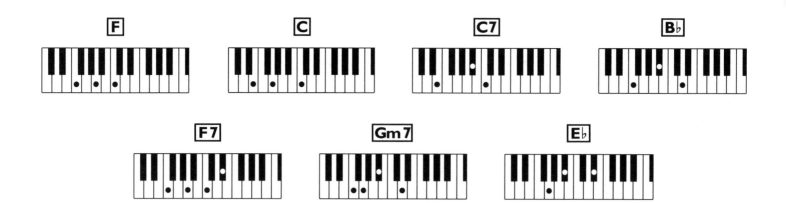

Voice: **Ocarina**

Rhythm: **Rock**

Tempo: ♩ = 96

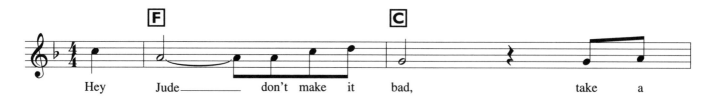

Hey Jude don't make it bad, take a

sad song and make it bet-ter. Re-mem-ber to let her in-to your

heart, then you can start to make it bet-ter.

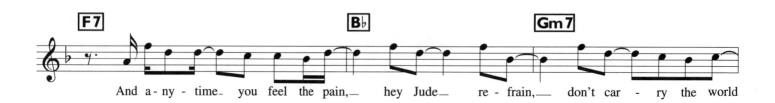

And a-ny-time you feel the pain, hey Jude re-frain, don't car-ry the world

upon your shoul - ders. For well you know that it's a fool

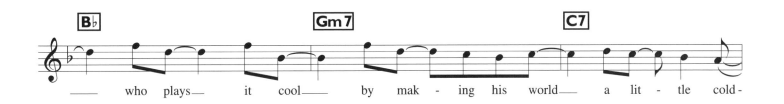

who plays it cool by mak - ing his world a lit - tle cold -

- er. Da da da da da da. Hey

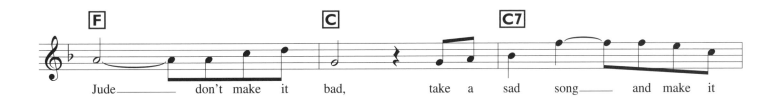

Jude don't make it bad, take a sad song and make it

bet - ter. Re - mem - ber to let her un - der your skin, then you be - gin

to make it bet - ter, bet - ter, bet - ter, bet - ter, bet - ter, bet - ter, oh.

Repeat to fade

Da da da da da da da, da da da da hey Jude.

I WILL SURVIVE

Words & Music by Dino Fekaris & Freddie Perren

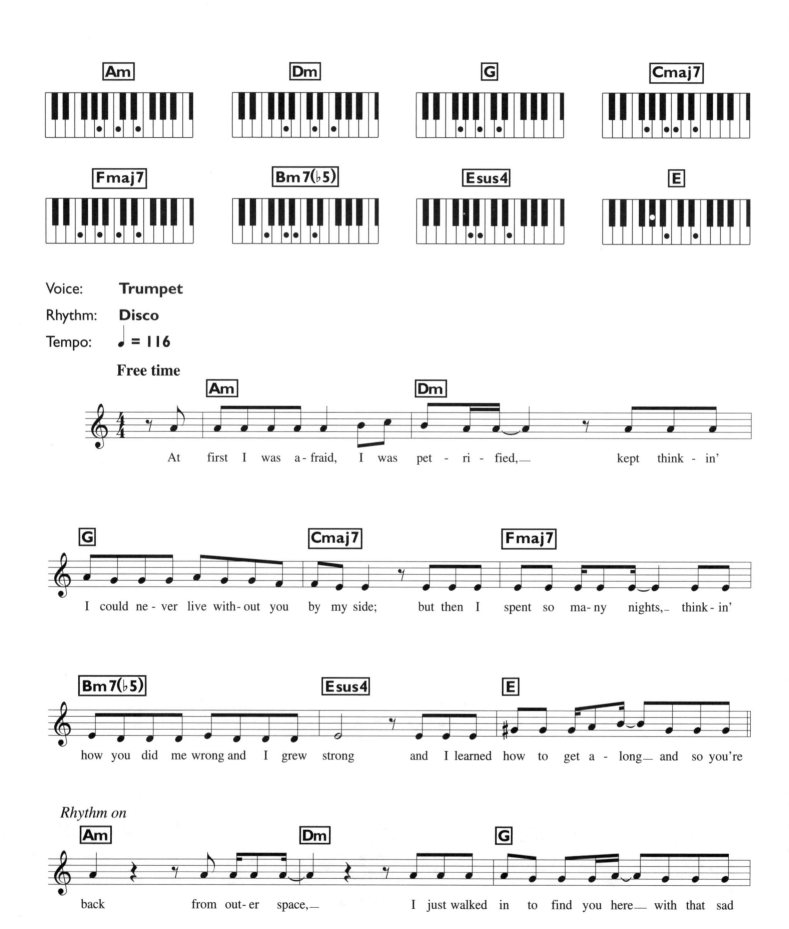

look up-on your face. I should have changed that stu-pid lock,— I should have made— you leave your key,— if I'd have known

— for just one se - cond you'd be back to bo-ther me.— Go on now go, walk out the door,

— just turn a - round— now, 'cause you're not wel - come a - ny - more.—

Weren't you the one— who tried to hurt— me with good-bye,— did I crum - ble, did you think I'd

lay down— and die? Oh no not I. I will sur - vive,———— oh, as

long as I know how to love— I know I'll stay a-live. I've got all my life to live,— I've got

all my love to give— and I'll sur - vive,— I will sur - vive.— I'll sur - vive.—

IMAGINE

Words & Music by John Lennon
© Copyright 1971 Lenono Music.
Administered by BMG Music Publishing Limited, Bedford House, 69-79 Fulham High Street, London SW6.
This arrangement © Copyright 1997 BMG Music Publishing Limited.
All Rights Reserved. International Copyright Secured.

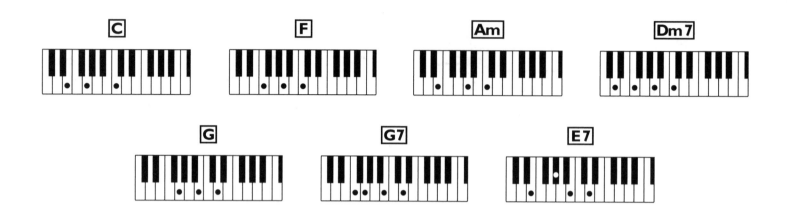

Voice: **Jazz Organ**

Rhythm: **Ballad**

Tempo: ♩ = 80

Im - a - gine there's no heav - en,

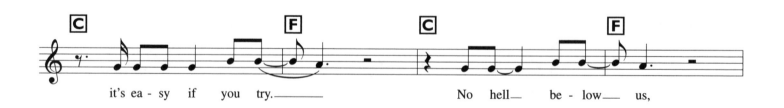

it's ea - sy if you try.⸺ No hell⸺ be - low⸺ us,

a - bove us on - ly sky.⸺ Im - a - gine all the peo-

IN THE AIR TONIGHT

Words & Music by Phil Collins
© Copyright 1981 Effectsound Limited/Hit & Run Music (Publishing) Limited, 30 Ives Street, London SW3.
All Rights Reserved. International Copyright Secured.

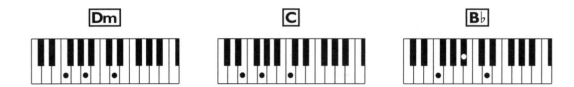

Voice: **Ocarina**

Rhythm: **Pop**

Tempo: ♩ = 96

Well if you told me— you were dreaming I would not lend— a hand.

I've seen your face— be-fore my— friend but I don't

know if you know— who I am.— Well I was there— and I saw—

— what you did, I saw it with my own two eyes.— So you can

wipe off that grin, I know where you've been,— it's all been a pack of lies.

EASIEST KEYBOARD COLLECTION

The Easiest Keyboard Books Ever!

Start playing all your favourite music today
with this great series of easy-play books
for electronic keyboard

**Hundreds of chart hits, ballads, love songs, film & TV themes,
showstoppers, jazz & blues standards, popular classics and more...**

EASIEST KEYBOARD COLLECTION

It's So Easy...

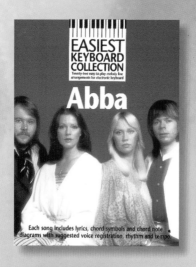
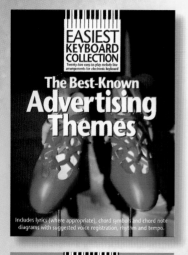
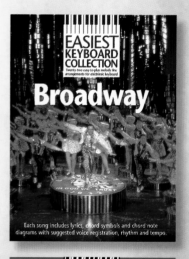
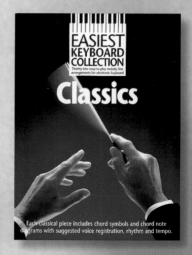

Christmas
Includes:
Frosty The Snowman
Mary's Boy Child
Silent Night
Winter Wonderland
Order No. AM952105

Classic Blues
Includes;
Basin Street Blues
Crazy
Georgia On My Mind
Memphis Blues
Order No. AM950697

Abba
Includes:
Chiquitita
Dancing Queen
Fernando
Take A Chance On Me
Order No. AM959860

Ballads
Includes:
Autumn Leaves
For The Good Times
Green, Green Grass Of Home
This Guy's In Love With You
Order No. AM952116

The Beatles
Includes:
Can't Buy Me Love
Eleanor Rigby
Lady Madonna
Yesterday
Order No. NO90686

The Best-Known Advertising Themes
Includes:
Female Of The Species (Impulse)
Flower Duet from Delibes' Lakmé
   (British Airways)
Guaglione (Guinness)
Marvellous (Renault Megane Scenic)
Order No. AM956550

The Best Party Hits
Includes:
Dizzy
Oops Upside Your Head
Saturday Night
Y.M.C.A.
Order No. AM955812

Boyzone
Includes:
A Different Beat
Father And Son
Love Me For A Reason
No Matter What
Order No. AM958331

Broadway
Includes:
Big Spender (Sweet Charity)
Empty Chairs At Empty Tables
   (Les Misérables)
Tonight (West Side Story)
What I Did For Love
   (A Chorus Line)
Order No. AM952127

Celine Dion
Includes:
Falling Into You
My Heart Will Go On
The Power Of Love
Think Twice
Order No. AM959850

Chart Hits
Includes:
Barbie Girl (Aqua)
I Believe I Can Fly (R. Kelly)
Picture Of You (Boyzone)
You Must Love Me (Madonna)
Order No. AM952083

Classics
Includes:
Air On The 'G' String
   (J.S. Bach)
Eine Kleine Nachtmusik -
   Themes (Mozart)
Ode To Joy from
   Symphony No.9 (Beethoven)
Swan Lake - Theme
   (Tchaikovsky)
Order No. AM952094

The Corrs
Includes:
Dreams
So Young
Someday
What Can I Do
Order No. AM959849

Disco Classics
Includes:
Disco Inferno (Trammps)
I Will Survive (Gloria Gaynor)
Night Fever (The Bee Gees)
Rasputin (Boney M)
Order No. AM959035

Can't read chord symbols? No problem...

Easy-to-follow keyboard diagrams are grouped together at the start of each piece
and show all the left-hand chord voicings used... it really couldn't be easier.

All the books in this great series contain 22 easy-to-play melody line arrangements, with no page turns to distract your concentration!

Suggested voice registration, automatic rhythm and tempo are given at the start of each piece and left-hand chord symbols with lyrics (where appropriate) are included with the music.

Elton John
Includes:
Candle In The Wind
Circle Of Life
Daniel
Song For Guy
Order No. AM958320

Film Themes
Includes:
A Whole New World (Aladdin)
Circle Of Life (The Lion King)
Love Is All Around
 (Four Weddings And A Funeral)
Speak Softly Love (The Godfather)
Order No. AM952050

Hits Of The 90s
Includes:
A Design For Life
 (Manic Street Preachers)
Ironic (Alanis Morissette)
Never Ever (All Saints)
Viva Forever (Spice Girls)
Order No. AM955780

Jazz Classics
Includes:
Don't Dream Of Anybody
 But Me (Li'l Darlin')
Fly Me To The Moon
Honeysuckle Rose
I'm Beginning To See The Light
Order No. AM952061

Love Songs
Includes:
Just The Two Of Us
Take My Breath Away
The Wind Beneath My Wings
Up Where We Belong
Order No. AM950708

Pop Classics
Includes:
A Whiter Shade Of Pale
 (Procol Harum)
Bridge Over Troubled Water
 (Simon & Garfunkel)
Hey Jude (The Beatles)
Massachusetts (The Bee Gees)
Order No. AM944196

Pop Hits
Includes:
Country House (Blur)
Money For Nothing (Dire Straits)
Rotterdam (Beautiful South)
Wonderful Tonight (Eric Clapton)
Order No. AM952072

Showstoppers
includes:
Consider Yourself (Oliver!)
Do You Hear The People Sing?
 (Les Misérables)
I Know Him So Well (Chess)
Maria (West Side Story)
Order No. AM944218

Sports Themes
Includes:
La Copa de la Vida (World Cup '98)
Nessun Dorma from Turandot
 (BBC World Cup '90)
Sporting Occasion
 (Wimbledon Closing Theme)
You'll Never Walk Alone
 (Football Anthem)
Order No. AM955801

Swing
Includes:
I Wan'na Be Like You
Lazy River
Moonlight Serenade
Take The 'A' Train
Order No. AM959101

TV Themes
Includes:
Casualty
EastEnders
Red Dwarf
The Black Adder
Order No. AM944207

60s Hits
Includes:
House Of The Rising Sun
 (The Animals)
Let's Dance (Chris Montez)
Only The Lonely (Roy Orbison)
Young Girl
 (Gary Puckett & Union Gap)
Order No. AM955768

80s Hits
Includes:
A Woman In Love (Barbra Streisand)
Eternal Flame (The Bangles)
Private Dancer (Tina Turner)
Who's That Girl? (Eurythmics)
Order No. AM955779

90s Hits
Includes:
Always (Bon Jovi)
Fields Of Gold (Sting)
When You Tell Me That
 You Love Me (Diana Ross)
Wonderwall (Oasis)
Order No. AM944229

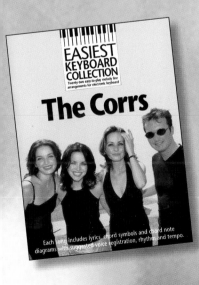

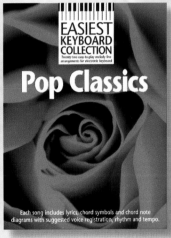

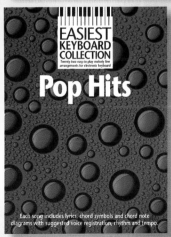

...Start Playing Right Away!

EASIEST KEYBOARD COLLECTION

Sample The Whole Series
With These Special Pop Selections...

Classic Chart Hits
46 all-time hit songs
including:
- A Whiter Shade Of Pale (Procol Harum)
- Baker Street (Gerry Rafferty)
- Bridge Over Troubled Water (Simon & Garfunkel)
- Candle In The Wind (Elton John)
- Can't Help Falling In Love (Elvis Presley)
- Can't Take My Eyes Off You (Andy Williams)
- Crazy (Patsy Cline)
- Eleanor Rigby (The Beatles)
- Every Breath You Take (The Police)
- I Will Survive (Gloria Gaynor)
- Imagine (John Lennon)
- Sailing (Rod Stewart)
- Tears In Heaven (Eric Clapton)
- Unchained Melody (The Righteous Brothers)
- Waterloo (Abba)

Order No. AM959904 (96pp.)

Pop Chart Hits
Over 40 more chart successes
including:
- A Different Beat (Boyzone)
- Falling Into You (Celine Dion)
- I Believe I Can Fly (R. Kelly)
- Last Thing On My Mind (Steps)
- Livin' La Vida Loca (Ricky Martin)
- Mambo No.5 (Lou Bega)
- Mi Chico Latino (Geri Halliwell)
- More Than A Woman (911)
- Perfect Moment (Martine McCutcheon)
- Say You'll Be There (Spice Girls)
- Search For The Hero (M People)
- Stay Another Day (East 17)
- What Can I Do? (The Corrs)
- When You're Gone (Bryan Adams & Mel. C)
- You Must Love Me (Madonna)

Order No. AM959893 (96pp.)

Top Chart Hits
Check out this special compact edition with over 90 pop hits
including:
- Barbie Girl (Aqua)
- Big Mistake (Natalie Imbruglia)
- Country House (Blur)
- Female Of The Species (Space)
- How Deep Is Your Love (Take That)
- Marvellous (Lightning Seeds)
- Rotterdam (Beautiful South)
- So Young (The Corrs)
- Take My Breath Away (Berlin)
- Wonderwall (Oasis)

Order No. AM962203 (192pp.)

Available from all good music retailers or, in case of difficulty, contact:

Music Sales Limited
Newmarket Road
Bury St. Edmunds
Suffolk IP33 3YB
Telephone 01284 725725
Fax 01284 702592

www.musicsales.com

PUB04642

I can feel it com - ing in the air to - night,___ oh Lord.___

And I've been wait-ing for this mo-ment for all my life,___ oh Lord.___

I can feel it___ in the air___ to-night, oh Lord,___ oh Lord.

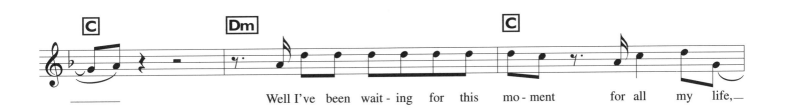

___ Well I've been wait - ing for this mo - ment for all my life,___

___ oh Lord.___ And I can feel it com -

- ing in the air to - night,___ oh Lord.___

Well I've been wait-ing for this mo-ment for all my life,___ oh Lord.___

JEALOUS GUY

Words & Music by John Lennon
© Copyright 1971 Lenono Music.
Administered by BMG Music Publishing Limited, Bedford House, 69-79 Fulham High Street, London SW6.
This arrangement © Copyright 1997 BMG Music Publishing Limited.
All Rights Reserved. International Copyright Secured.

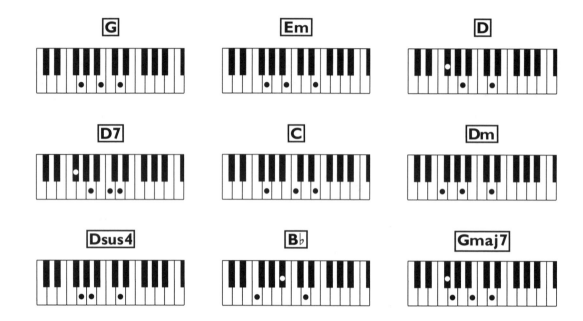

Voice: **Clarinet**

Rhythm: **Rock**

Tempo: ♩ = 80

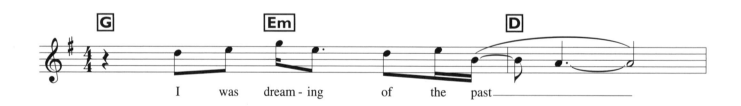

I was dream-ing of the past

and my heart was beat - ing fast.

I be - gan to lose con - trol,

I be-gan ____ to lose ____ con - trol.

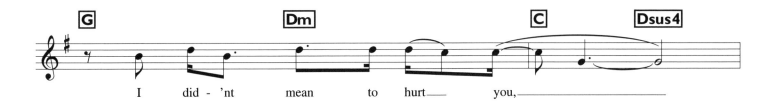

I did-'nt mean to hurt ____ you, ____

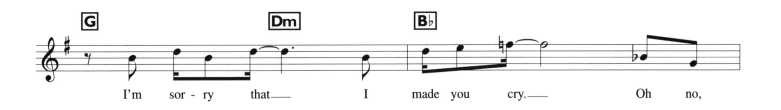

I'm sor-ry that ____ I made you cry. ____ Oh no,

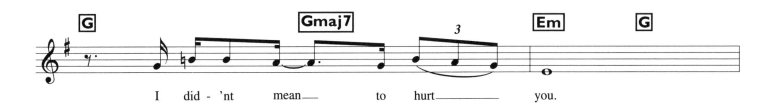

I did-'nt mean ____ to hurt ____ you.

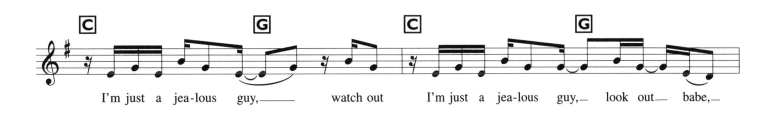

I'm just a jea-lous guy, ____ watch out I'm just a jea-lous guy, ____ look out ____ babe, ____

I'm just a jea-lous guy. ____

MASSACHUSETTS

Words & Music by Barry Gibb, Robin Gibb & Maurice Gibb

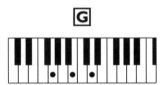
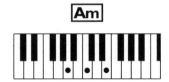
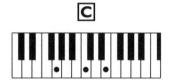

Voice: **Trumpet**

Rhythm: **Pop**

Tempo: ♩ = 96

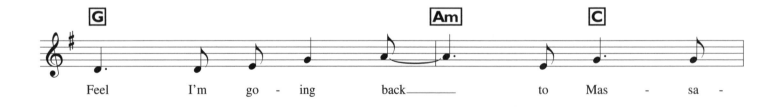

Feel   I'm go - ing   back_____   to   Mas - sa -

- chu - setts;   some - thing's tell - ing me_____

_____   I   must   go   home._____

And   the   lights   all   went

out   in   Mas -   -   sa -   chu -   -   setts,

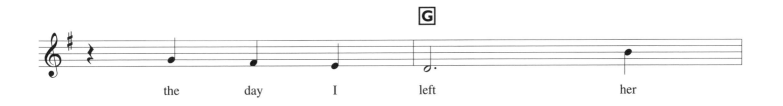
the   day   I   left   her

stand -   ing   on   her   own.

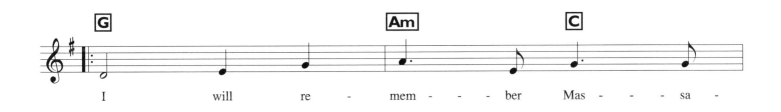
I   will   re -   mem -   -   ber   Mas -   -   sa -

Repeat to fade

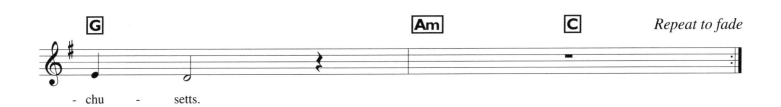
- chu -   setts.

MONEY FOR NOTHING

Words & Music by Mark Knopfler & Sting

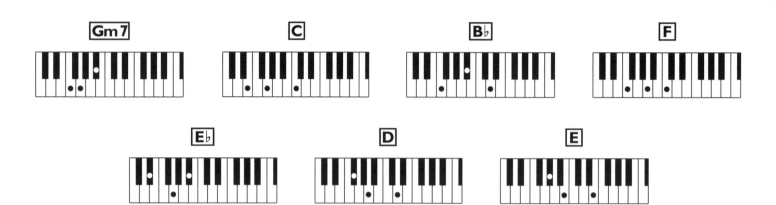

Voice: **Saxophone**

Rhythm: **Rock**

Tempo: ♩ = 132

Now look at them— yo - yo's that's—

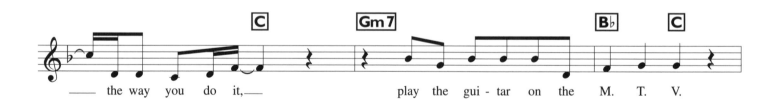

—— the way you do it,—— play the gui - tar on the M. T. V.

that ain't—— work - in', that's—— the way you do it, mo - ney for no - thin' and the

chicks for free.—— That ain't work - in', that's—— the way you do it

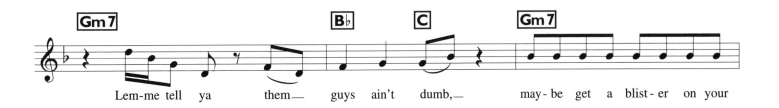

Lem-me tell ya them— guys ain't dumb,— may-be get a blist-er on your

lit - tle fing-er, may - be get a blist-er on your— thumb.—

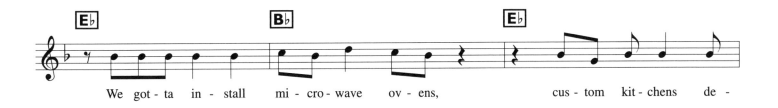

We got-ta in - stall mi - cro - wave ov - ens, cus - tom kit - chens de -

- li - ver - ies._____ We got - ta move these re - frig - er - a - tors,

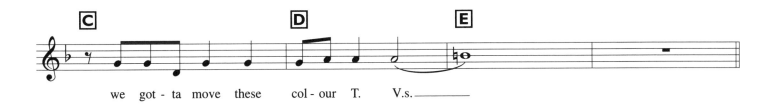

we got - ta move these col - our T. V.s._____

Mo - ney for no - thin', chicks for free.—

Repeat to fade

Mo - ney for no - thin' and chicks for free.—

MR TAMBOURINE MAN

Words & Music by Bob Dylan

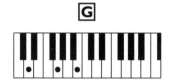
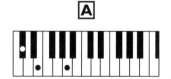
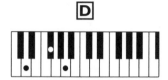
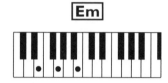

Voice: **Harmonica**

Rhythm: **16 Beat**

Tempo: ♩ = **104**

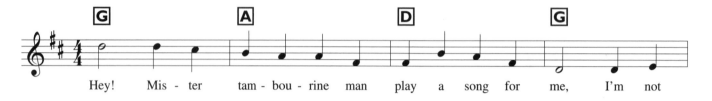

Hey! Mis-ter tam-bou-rine man play a song for me, I'm not

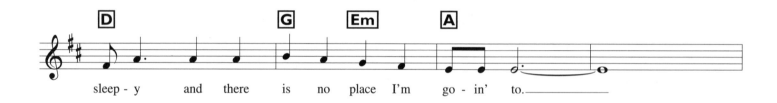

sleep-y and there is no place I'm go-in' to.

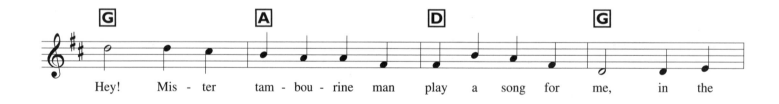

Hey! Mis-ter tam-bou-rine man play a song for me, in the

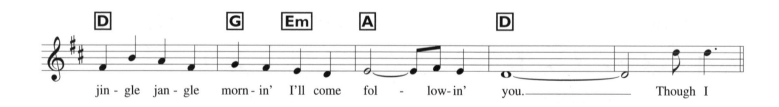

jin-gle jan-gle morn-in' I'll come fol-low-in' you. Though I

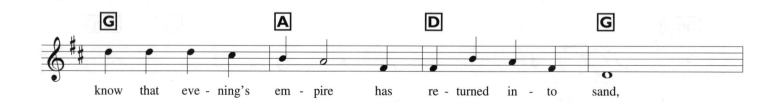

know that eve-ning's em-pire has re-turned in-to sand,

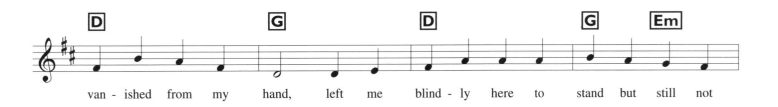

van - ished from my hand, left me blind - ly here to stand but still not

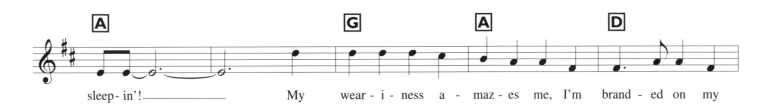

sleep - in'!_____ My wear - i - ness a - maz - es me, I'm brand - ed on my

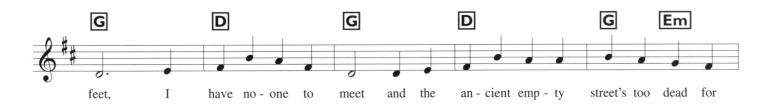

feet, I have no - one to meet and the an - cient emp - ty street's too dead for

dream - in'._____ Hey! Mis - ter tam - bou - rine man

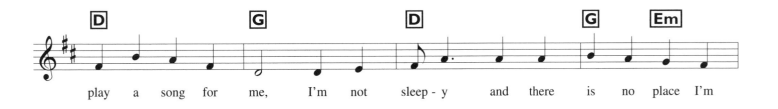

play a song for me, I'm not sleep - y and there is no place I'm

go - in' to._____ Hey! Mis - ter tam - bou - rine man play a song for

me, in the jin - gle jan - gle morn - in' I'll come fol - low - in' you.

MULL OF KINTYRE

Words & Music by McCartney & Laine
© Copyright 1977 by MPL Communications Limited,
Administered by MPL Communications Limited, by arrangement with ATV Music.
All Rights Reserved. International Copyright Secured.

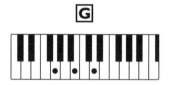 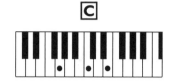  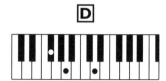

Voice: **Jazz Organ**

Rhythm: **Jazz Waltz**

Tempo: ♩ = 120

Mull of Kin - tyre, oh mist roll - ing

in from___ the sea, my de - sire is

al - ways to be here, oh Mull of Kin -

- tyre.

Far have I trav - elled and much have I

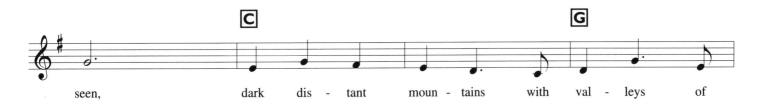

seen, dark dis - tant moun - tains with val - leys of

green. Past paint - ed des - erts, the sun - set's on

fire as he car - ries me home to the Mull of Kin -

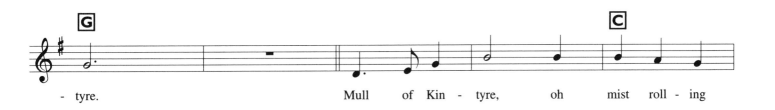

- tyre. Mull of Kin - tyre, oh mist roll - ing

in from the sea, my de - sire is al - ways to

be here, oh Mull of Kin - tyre.

Repeat to fade

OB-LA-DI, OB-LA-DA

Words & Music by John Lennon & Paul McCartney

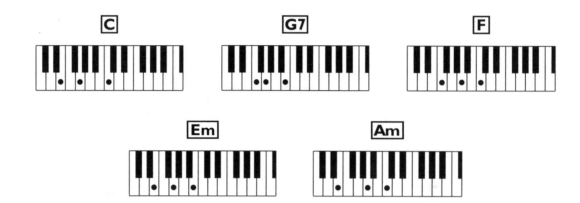

Voice: **Accordion**

Rhythm: **2 Beat**

Tempo: ♩ = 120

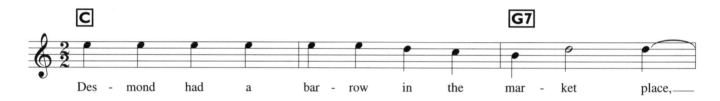

Des - mond had a bar - row in the mar - ket place, ____

____ Mol - - - ly is the sing - er in a

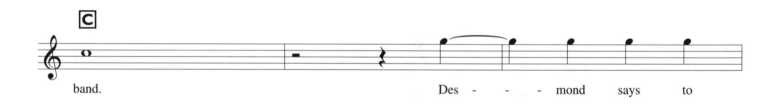

band. Des - - - mond says to

Mol - ly "Girl I like your face", ____ and Mol - ly

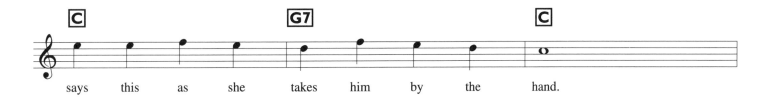

says this as she takes him by the hand.

Ob - la - di, ob - la - da, life goes on,

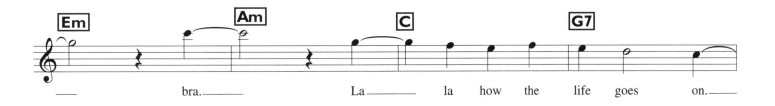

bra. La la how the life goes on.

Ob - la - di, ob - la - da, life goes on,

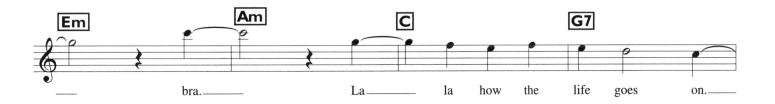

bra. La la how the life goes on.

And if you want some fun

take ob - la - di - bla - da.

OH, PRETTY WOMAN

Words & Music by Roy Orbison & Bill Dees

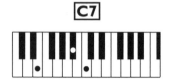 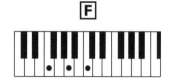  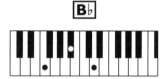

C7   **F**   **Dm**   **Bb**

Voice: **Saxophone**

Rhythm: **Rock 'n' Roll**

Tempo: ♩ = 116

Pret - ty

wo - man, — walk - ing down the street, — pret - ty wo - man, — the kind I

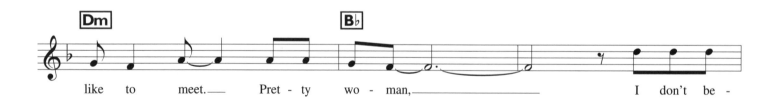

like to meet. — Pret - ty wo - man, — I don't be -

- lieve you, — you're not the truth. — No - one could look as good as

you. —

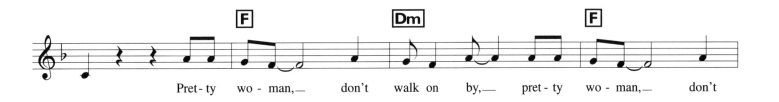

Pret - ty wo - man,— don't walk on by,— pret - ty wo - man,— don't

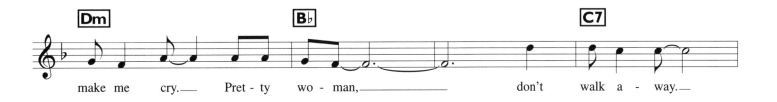

make me cry.— Pret - ty wo - man,——————— don't walk a - way.—

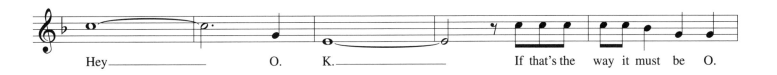

Hey——————— O. K.——————— If that's the way it must be O.

K.——————— I guess I'll go on home, it's late. There'll be to - mor - row night, but

wait! What do I see,——————————————— is she

walk - ing back to me?——————— Yeah—— she's walk - ing back to

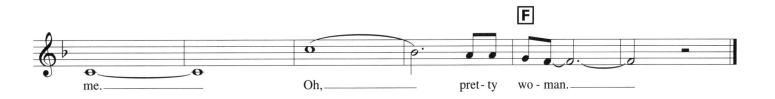

me.——————— Oh,——————— pret - ty wo - man.———————

SAILING

Words & Music by Gavin Sutherland
© Copyright 1972 by Island Music Limited, 47 British Grove, London W4.
All Rights Reserved. International Copyright Secured.

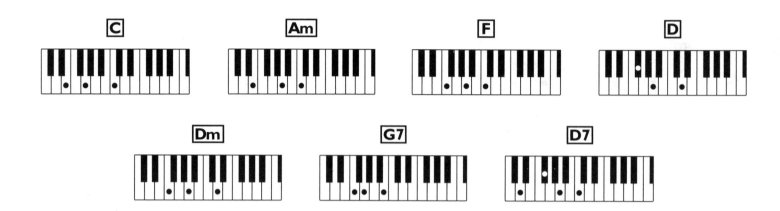

Voice: **Flute**

Rhythm: **16 beat**

Tempo: ♩ = **76**

I am sail - ing, I am sail - ing, home a -

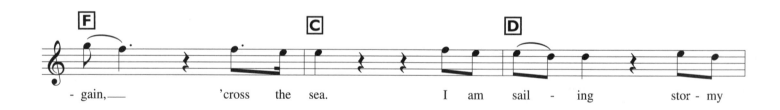

- gain, ——— 'cross the sea. I am sail - ing stor - my

wa - ters, to be near——— you, to be free. I am

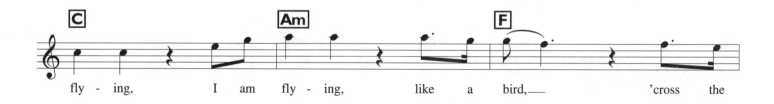

fly - ing, I am fly - ing, like a bird, ——— 'cross the

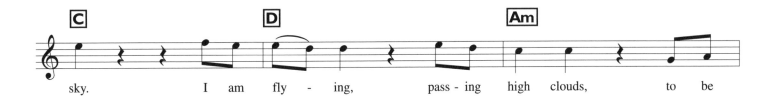

sky.   I am fly - ing,   pass - ing high clouds,   to be

with__ you,   to be free.   Can you hear me,   can you

hear me, through the dark__ night far a - way.   I am

dy - ing,__ for - ev - er try - ing to be with__ you, who can

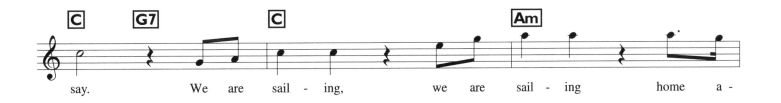

say.   We are sail - ing,   we are sail - ing home a -

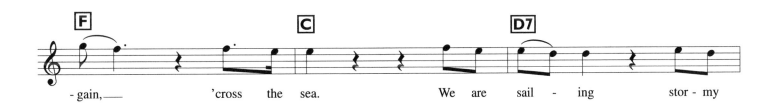

- gain,__   'cross the sea.   We are sail - ing stor - my

wa - ters   to be near__ you,   to be free.

STARS

Words & Music by Mick Hucknall
© Copyright 1991 So What Limited, UK.
Sub-published by So What Limited/EMI Songs Limited, London WC2H 0EA.
All Rights Reserved. International Copyright Secured.

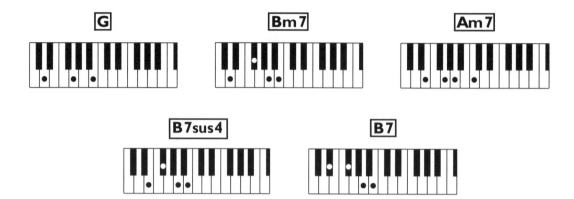

Voice: **Jazz Organ**

Rhythm: **Soul Ballad**

Tempo: ♩ = 104

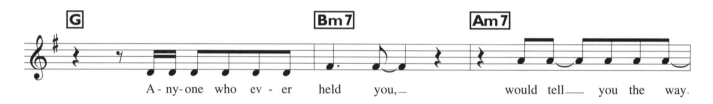

A - ny-one who ev - er held you,— would tell— you the way.

—— I'm feel - ing, a - ny-one who ev - er want - ed you,

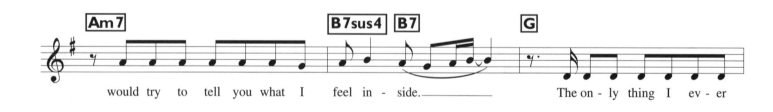

would try to tell you what I feel in - side.—— The on - ly thing I ev - er

want - ed—— was the feel-ing that you—— ain't fak - ing.

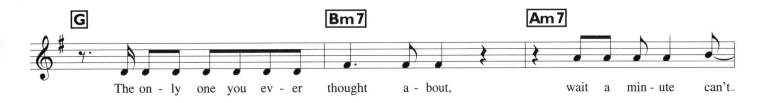

The on - ly one you ev - er thought a - bout, wait a min - ute can't_

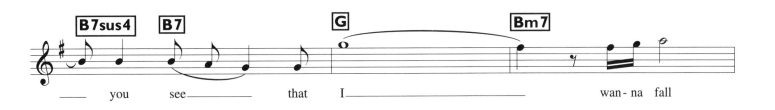

_ you see_ that I_ wan - na fall

from the stars_ straight in - to your_ arms._ I,_

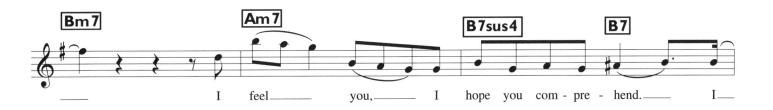

_ I feel_ you,_ I hope you com - pre - hend._ I_

_ wan - na fall_ from the stars_

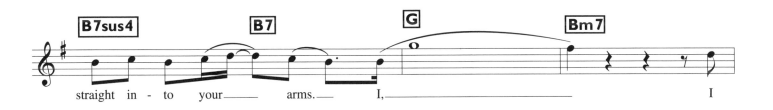

straight in - to your_ arms._ I,_ I

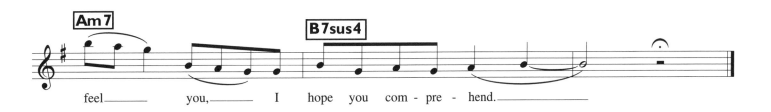

feel_ you, I hope you com - pre - hend._

THE WINNER TAKES IT ALL

Words & Music by Benny Andersson & Bjorn Ulvaeus

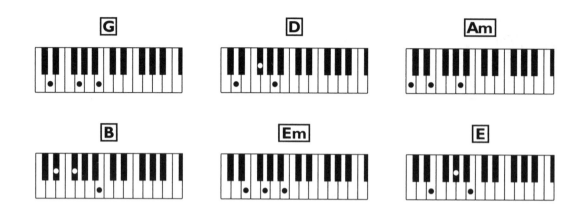

Voice: **Piano**

Rhythm: **Ballad**

Tempo: ♩ = 108

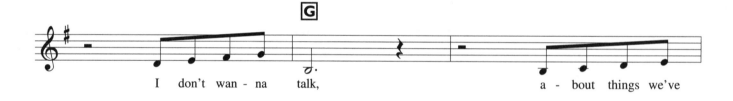

I don't wan - na talk, a - bout things we've

gone through, though it's hurt - ing me,

now it's his - to - ry. I've played all my

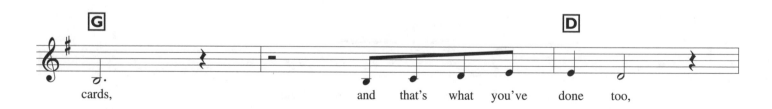

cards, and that's what you've done too,

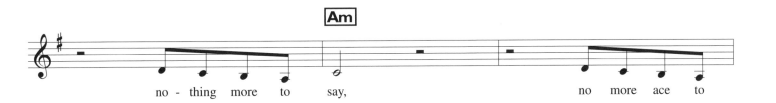
no - thing more to say, no more ace to

play. The win - ner takes it all,

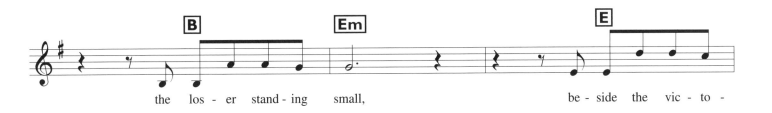
the los - er stand - ing small, be - side the vic - to -

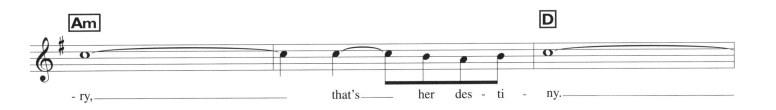
- ry, that's her des - ti - ny.

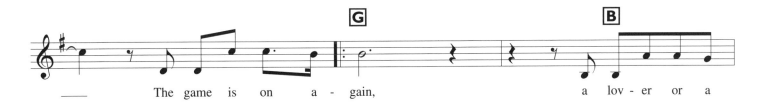
The game is on a - gain, a lov - er or a

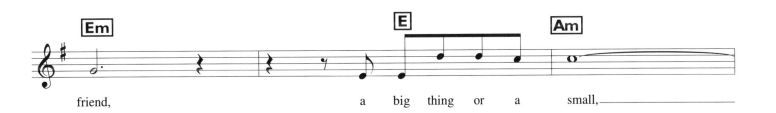
friend, a big thing or a small,

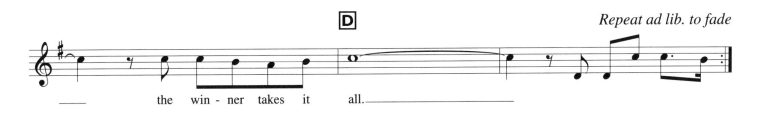
Repeat ad lib. to fade

the win - ner takes it all.

WITH A LITTLE HELP FROM MY FRIENDS

Words & Music by John Lennon & Paul McCartney
© Copyright 1967 Northern Songs.
All Rights Reserved. International Copyright Secured.

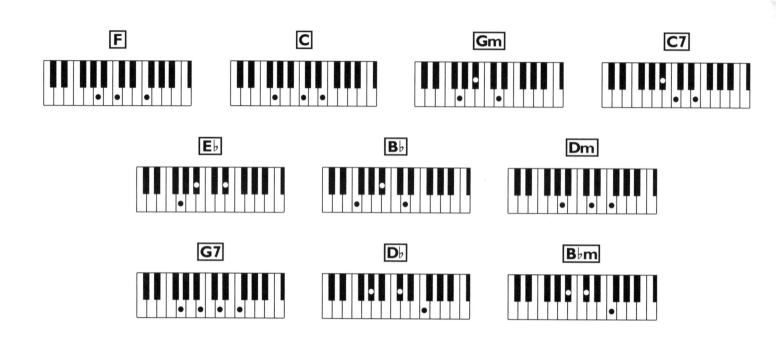

Voice: **Clarinet**

Rhythm: **2 Beat**

Tempo: ♩ = 120

What would you do —— if I sang —— out of tune? Would you stand ——

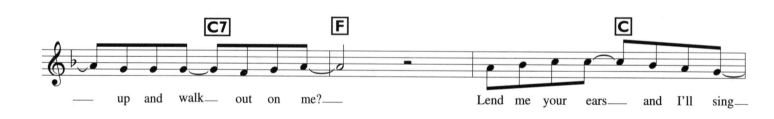

—— up and walk —— out on me? —— Lend me your ears —— and I'll sing ——

—— you a song —— and I'll try —— not to sing —— out of key. —— Oh, I get by ——

— with a lit-tle help— from my friends.— Mm, I get high— with a lit-tle help— from my friends.

— Mm, I'm gon-na try— with a lit-tle help— from my friends.— (Do you need— a-ny-bo-

-dy?) I need some-bo-dy to love.— (Could it be— a-ny-bo-

-dy?) I want some-bo-dy to love.— Oh, I get by— with a lit-tle help— from my friends.

— Mm, I'm gon-na try— with a lit-tle help— from my friends.— Oh I get high—

— with a lit-tle help— from my friends.— Yes I get by— with a lit-tle help— from my friends,

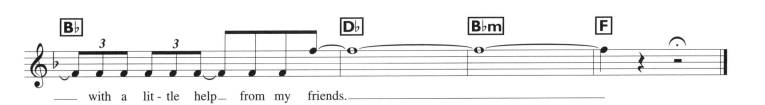

— with a lit-tle help— from my friends.—

10/01 (41588)

EASIEST KEYBOARD COLLECTION

Easy-to-play melody line arrangements for all keyboards with chord symbols and lyrics Suggested registration, rhythm and tempo are included for each song together with keyboard diagrams showing left-hand chord voicings used.

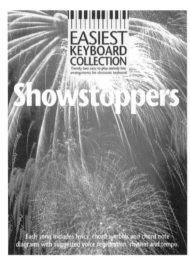

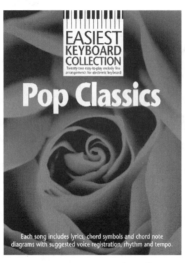

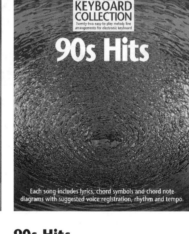

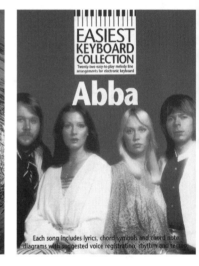

Showstoppers

Consider Yourself (Oliver!), Do You Hear The People Sing? (Les Misérables), I Know Him So Well (Chess), Maria (West Side Story), Smoke Gets In Your Eyes (Roberta) and 17 more big stage hits.
Order No. AM944218

Pop Classics

A Whiter Shade Of Pale (Procol Harum), Bridge Over Troubled Water (Simon & Garfunkel), Crocodile Rock (Elton John) and 19 more classic hit songs, including Hey Jude (The Beatles), Imagine (John Lennon), and Massachusetts (The Bee Gees).
Order No. AM944196

90s Hits

Over 20 of the greatest hits of the 1990s, including Always (Bon Jovi), Fields Of Gold (Sting), Have I Told You Lately (Rod Stewart), One Sweet Day (Mariah Carey), Say You'll Be There (Spice Girls), and Wonderwall (Oasis).
Order No. AM944229

Abba

A great collection of 22 Abba hit songs. Includes: Dancing Queen, Fernando, I Have A Dream, Mamma Mia, Super Trouper, Take A Chance On Me, Thank You For The Music, The Winner Takes It All, and Waterloo.
Order No. AM959860

Also available...

Ballads, Order No. AM952116	**The Corrs**, Order No. AM959849
The Beatles, Order No. NO90686	**Elton John**, Order No. AM958320
Boyzone, Order No. AM958331	**Film Themes**, Order No. AM952050
Broadway, Order No. AM952127	**Hits of the 90s,** Order No. AM955780
Celine Dion, Order No. AM959850	**Jazz Classics**, Order No. AM952061
Chart Hits, Order No. AM952083	**Love Songs**, Order No. AM950708
Christmas, Order No. AM952105	**Pop Hits**, Order No. AM952072
Classic Blues, Order No. AM950697	**60s Hits**, Order No. AM955768
Classics, Order No. AM952094	**80s Hits**, Order No. AM955779

...plus many more!